武満徹
ピアノのための
雨の樹素描Ⅱ
──オリヴィエ・メシアンの追憶に──

TORU TAKEMITSU
RAIN TREE SKETCH Ⅱ
── In Memoriam Olivier Messiaen ──

for piano

SJ 1072

© 1992, Schott Music Co. Ltd., Tokyo
International Copyright Secured.
All Rights Reserved.

T0050695

SCHOTT

オリヴィエ・メシアンの追憶に。

1992年10月24日、オルレアン国際音楽祭(フランス)でおこなわれた「オリヴィエ・メシアン追悼演奏会」のために作曲され、アラン・ヌヴーにより初演された。

演奏時間—— 5 分

In Memoriam Olivier Messiaen

Composed for a concert "Hommage à Olivier Messiaen" of Les Semaines Musicales Internationales d'Orléans, France and premiered by Alain Neveux on October 24, 1992.

Duration: 5 minutes

Rain Tree Sketch II
— In Memoriam Olivier Messiaen —

雨の樹素描 II
——オリヴィエ・メシアンの追憶に——
for piano

Toru Takemitsu
武満 徹

©1992, Schott Music Co. Ltd., Tokyo

4

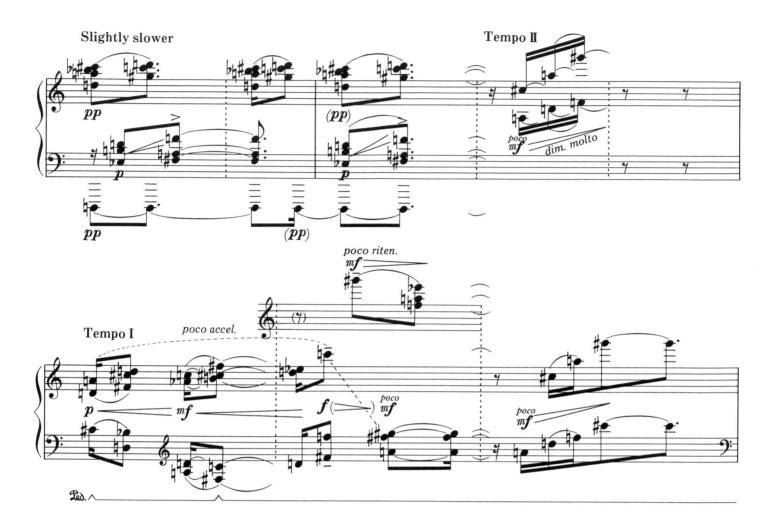

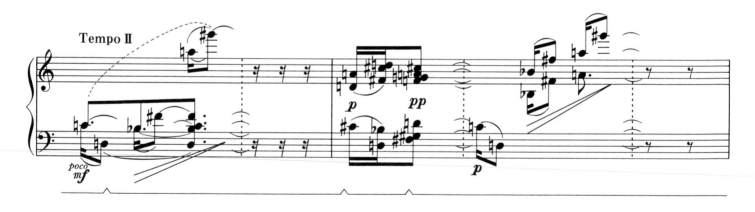

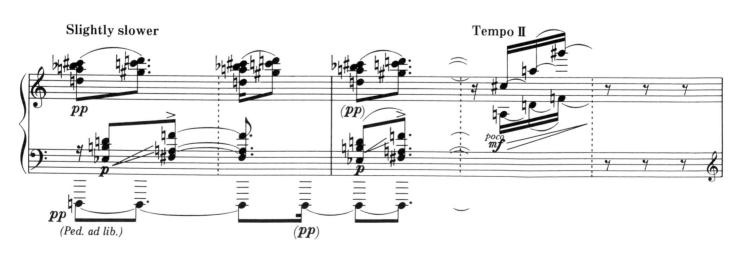

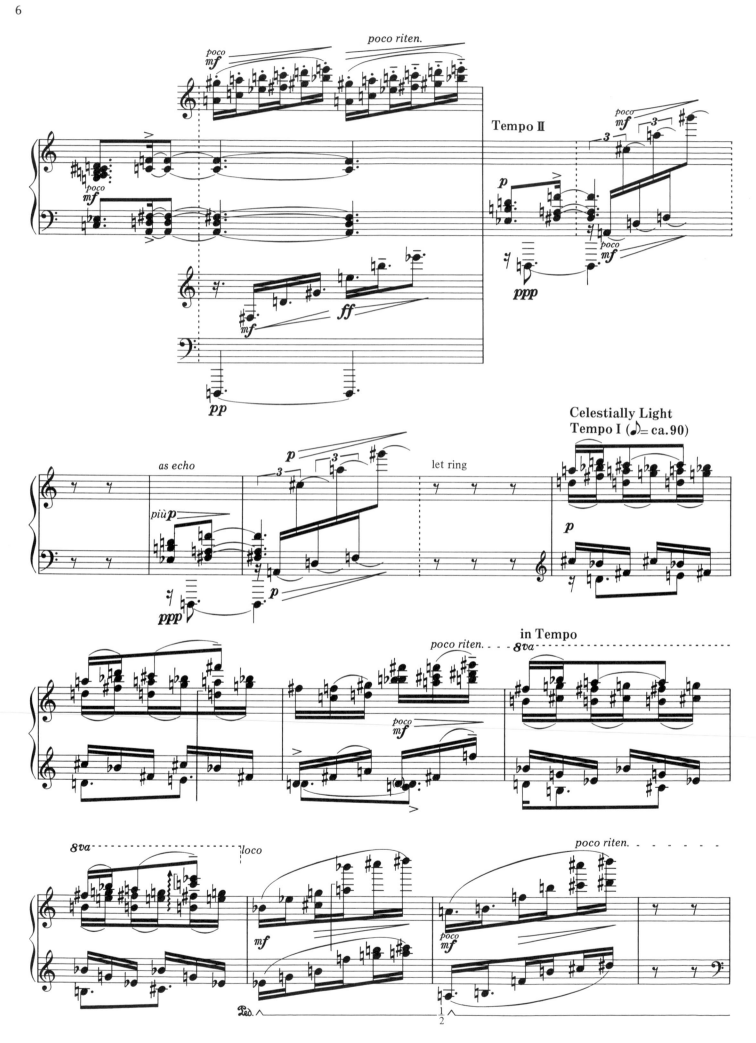

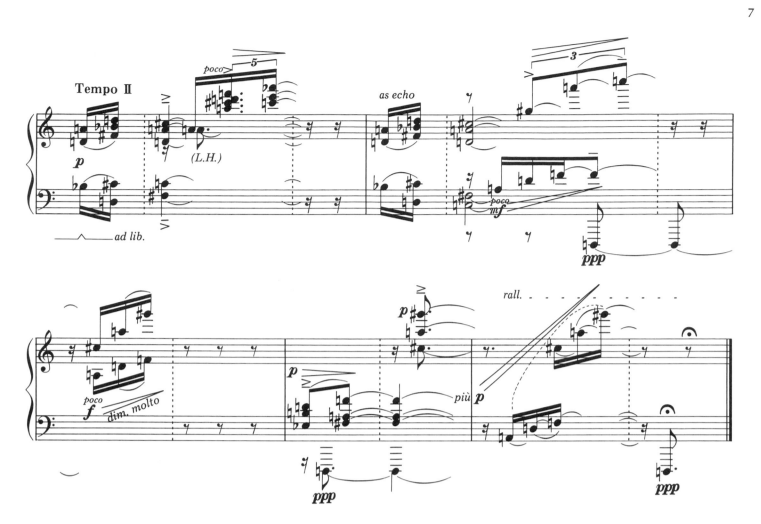

武満 徹《雨の樹素描Ⅱ》　　　●

ピアノのための

初版発行————————————————————1992年10月25日

第1版第13刷⑬ ————————————2022年8月5日

発行————————————————ショット・ミュージック株式会社

—————————————————東京都千代田区内神田1-10-1 平富ビル3階

—————————————————〒101-0047

—————————————————(03)6695-2450

—————————————————www.schottjapan.com

—————————————————ISBN 978-4-89066-372-9

—————————————————ISMN M-65001-109-9